Ernest H. Shepard

WINNIE~THE~POOH
VISITORS BOOK

A.A. Milne with sketches by E.H. Shepard

METHUEN

'The animals in the stories came for the most part from the nursery . . . Shepard drew them, as one might say, from the living model. They were what they are for anyone to see; I described rather than invented them.'

A.A. MILNE

Eeyore
state grey

Date	Name	Address

Date	Name	Address

Date	Name	Address

Kanga & Roo

from life 1926
E.H. Shepard

Date	Name	Address

Date	Name	Address

Here is Edward Bear, coming downstairs now, bump, bump, bump, on the back of his head, behind Christopher Robin. It is, as far as he knows, the only way of coming downstairs, but sometimes he feels that there really is another way, if only he could stop bumping for a moment and think of it. And then he feels that perhaps there isn't. Anyhow, here he is at the bottom, and ready to be introduced to you. Winnie-the-Pooh.

"But you don't get honey with balloons!"
"*I* do," said Pooh.

Date	Name	Address

Date	Name	Address

How sweet to be a Cloud
    Floating in the Blue!
Every little cloud
Always sings aloud.

Date	Name	Address

Date	Name	Address

"*Ow!*" said Pooh.
"Did I miss?" you asked.
"You didn't exactly *miss*," said Pooh,
"but you missed the *balloon*."

Date	Name	Address

Bear began to sigh, and then found he couldn't because he was so tightly stuck;
and a tear rolled down his eye, as he said:
"Then would you read a Sustaining Book, such as would help and comfort a
Wedged Bear in Great Tightness?"
So for a week Christopher Robin read that sort of book at the North end of Pooh,
and Rabbit hung his washing on the South end . . . and in between Bear felt himself
getting slenderer and slenderer.

Date	Name	Address

Pooh always liked a little something
at eleven o'clock in the morning,
and he was very glad to see Rabbit
getting out the plates and mugs;
and when Rabbit said, "Honey or
condensed milk with your bread?"
he was so excited that he said, "Both."

Date	Name	Address

So he started to climb out of the hole.
He pulled with his front paws, and
pushed with his back paws, and in a
little while his nose was out in the open
again . . . and then his ears . . . and then
his front paws . . . and then his shoulders . . .
and then —

Date	Name	Address

"Oh, help!" said Pooh.
"I'd better go back."
"Oh, bother!" said Pooh.
"I shall have to go on."
"I can't do either!" said Pooh.
"Oh, help *and* bother!"

Date	Name	Address

He had made up a little hum that very morning,
as he was doing his Stoutness Exercises
in front of the glass: *Tra-la-la, tra-la-la,*
as he stretched up as high as he could go,
and then *Tra-la-la, tra-la — oh, help! —*
la, as he tried to reach his toes.

Date	Name	Address

And Pooh looked at the knocker and the
notice below it, and he looked at the
bell-rope and the notice below it, and
the more he looked at the bell-rope,
the more he felt that he had seen something
like it, somewhere else, sometime before.
"Handsome bell-rope, isn't it?" said Owl.
Pooh nodded.
"It reminds me of something," he said,
"but I can't think what. Where did you get it?"
"I just came across it in the Forest.
It was hanging over a bush."

"Well, either a tail *is* there or it isn't there. You can't make a mistake about it, and yours *isn't* there!"
"Then what is?"
"Nothing."

Date	Name	Address

Date	Name	Address

"Let's have a look," said Eeyore, and he turned slowly round to the place where his tail had been a little while ago, and then, finding that he couldn't catch it up, he turned round the other way, until he came back to where he was at first.

Date	Name	Address

When Christopher Robin had nailed it on in its right place again, Eeyore frisked about the forest, waving his tail so happily that Winnie-the-Pooh came over all funny, and had to hurry home for a little snack of something to sustain him.

Date	Name	Address

Date	Name	Address

Eeyore, the old grey Donkey,
stood by the side of the stream,
and looked at himself in the water.
"Pathetic," he said.
"That's what it is. Pathetic."
He turned and walked slowly
down the stream for twenty
yards, splashed across it,
and walked slowly back on
the other side. Then he looked
at himself in the water again.
"As I thought," he said.
"No better from *this* side."

"Good morning, Eeyore," said Pooh.
"Good morning, Pooh Bear," said Eeyore
gloomily.
"If it *is* a good morning," he said.
"Which I doubt," said he.

Date	Name	Address

Date	Name	Address

He held it very tightly against himself,
so that it shouldn't blow away,
and he ran as fast as he could so
as to get to Eeyore before Pooh did.
And running along, and thinking how
pleased Eeyore would be, he didn't
look where he was going . . .

Date	Name	Address

"I'm very glad," said Pooh happily,
"that I thought of giving you a
Useful Pot to put things in."

Date	Name	Address

"I'm very glad," said Piglet happily,
"that I thought of giving you
Something to put in a Useful Pot."

Date	Name	Address

Kanga and Roo were spending a quiet afternoon in a sandy part of the Forest.
Baby Roo was practising very small jumps in the sand, and falling down mouse-holes
and climbing out of them, and Kanga was fidgeting about and saying "Just one more
jump, dear, and then we must go home." And at that moment who should come
stumping up the hill but Pooh.
"Good afternoon, Kanga."
"Good afternoon, Pooh."
"Look at me jumping," squeaked Roo, and fell into another mouse-hole.

Date	Name	Address

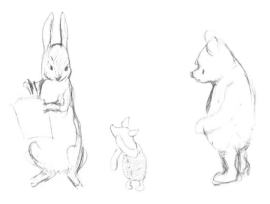

"It is hard to be brave," said Piglet,
sniffing slightly, "when you're only
a Very Small Animal."

Date	Name	Address

Date	Name	Address

"Now then, into the bath, and don't let me
have to speak to you about it again."
Before he knew where he was, Piglet was
in the bath, and Kanga was scrubbing him
firmly with a large lathery flannel.

Date	Name	Address

Date	Name	Address

"Pooh's found the North Pole,"
said Christopher Robin. "Isn't that lovely?"
 Pooh looked modestly down.
 "Is that it?" said Eeyore.
 "Yes," said Christopher Robin.
 "Is that what we were looking for?"
 "Yes," said Pooh.
 "Oh!" said Eeyore. "Well, anyhow — it didn't rain," he said.
 They stuck the pole into the ground, and Christopher Robin
tied a message on to it.

Christopher Robin was sitting outside
his door, putting on his Big Boots.
As soon as he saw the Big Boots, Pooh knew
that an Adventure was going to happen.

Date	Name	Address

Date	Name	Address

The Piglet was sitting on the ground
at the door of his house blowing happily
at a dandelion, and wondering whether
it would be this year, next year,
sometime or never.

Date	Name	Address

Date	Name	Address

Date	Name	Address

Every morning he went out with his umbrella and put a stick in the place where the water came up to, and every next morning he went out and couldn't see his stick any more, so he put another stick in the place where the water came up to, and then he walked home again, and each morning he had a shorter way to walk than he had had the morning before. On the morning of the fifth day he saw the water all round him, and knew that for the first time in his life he was on a real island. Which was very exciting.

Date	Name	Address

Date	Name	Address

Then he had an idea, and I think
that for a Bear of Very Little Brain,
it was a good idea. He said to himself:
"If a bottle can float, then a jar can
float, and if a jar floats, I can sit on the
top of it, if it's a very big jar."

Date	Name	Address

Date	Name	Address

He opened his umbrella and put it point downwards in the water. It floated but wobbled. Pooh got in. . . Then they both got in together, and it wobbled no longer. "I shall call this boat *The Brain of Pooh*," said Christopher Robin.

Date	Name	Address

"This party," said Christopher Robin, "is a party because of what someone did, and we all know who it was, and it's his party, because of what he did, and I've got a present for him and here it is." Then he felt about a little and whispered, "Where is it?". . . "Here it is!" cried Christopher Robin excitedly.

"Pass it down to silly old Pooh. It's for Pooh."

"For Pooh?" said Eeyore.

"Of course it is. The best bear in all the world."

"A party for Me?" thought Pooh to himself.
"How grand!" And he began to wonder if all
the other animals would know that it was
a special Pooh Party.

Date	Name	Address

"Eeyore," said Owl, "Christopher Robin
is giving a party."
"Very interesting," said Eeyore. "I suppose they will be
sending me down the odd bits which got trodden on.
Kind and Thoughtful. Not at all, don't mention it."

Date	Name	Address

Date	Name	Address

Kanga said to Roo, "Drink up your milk first dear, and talk afterwards." So Roo, who was drinking his milk, tried to say that he could do both at once . . . and had to be patted on the back and dried for quite a long time afterwards.

Date	Name	Address

In a little while Piglet was wearing a white muffler round his neck and feeling more snowy behind the ears than he had ever felt before.

Date	Name	Address

"We will build it here," said Pooh,
"just by this wood, out of the wind,
because this is where I thought of it.
And we will call this Pooh Corner.
And we will build an Eeyore House
with sticks at Pooh Corner for Eeyore."

Date	Name	Address

Date	Name	Address

"What with all this snow and one thing and another,
not to mention icicles and such-like, it isn't so
Hot in my field about three o'clock in the morning."

Date	Name	Address

"Hallo!" said Tigger.
"I've found somebody just like me. I thought
I was the only one of them."

Date	Name	Address

Tigger took a large mouthful of honey . . . and he looked up at the ceiling with his head on one side, and made exploring noises with his tongue, and considering noises, and what-have-we-got-*here* noises . . . and then he said in a very decided voice: "Tiggers don't like honey."

Date	Name	Address

Date	Name	Address

Date	Name	Address

Eeyore led the way to the most thistly-looking patch
of thistles that ever was, and waved a hoof at it.
"Help yourself, Tigger."
Tigger thanked him and looked a little anxiously at Pooh.
"Are these really thistles?" he whispered.
"Yes," said Pooh.
"What Tiggers like best?"
"That's right," said Pooh.

Date	Name	Address

"Come along," called Christopher Robin.
"You'll be all right."
"Just wait a moment," said Tigger
nervously. "Small piece of bark in my eye."
And he moved slowly along his branch.
"Come on, it's easy!" squeaked Roo.
And suddenly Tigger found how easy it was.
"Ow!" he shouted as the tree flew past him.
"Look out!" shouted Christopher Robin
to the others.
There was a crash, and a tearing noise,
and a confused heap of everybody
on the ground.

Date	Name	Address

Date	Name	Address

Pooh was sitting in his house one day,
counting his pots of honey, when there came
a knock on the door.
"Fourteen," said Pooh. "Come in. Fourteen.
Or was it fifteen? Bother. That's muddled me."

Date	Name	Address

Date	Name	Address

"I'm planting a haycorn, Pooh, so that it can
grow up into an oak-tree, and have lots of
haycorns just outside the front door instead
of having to walk miles and miles, do you see, Pooh?"
"Supposing it doesn't?" said Pooh.

Date	Name	Address

It suddenly came over him that nobody had ever picked Eeyore a bunch of violets, and the more he thought of this, the more he thought how sad it was to be an Animal who had never had a bunch of violets picked for him. So he hurried out again, saying to himself, "Eeyore, Violets" and then "Violets, Eeyore," in case he forgot, because it was that sort of day, and he picked a large bunch and trotted along, smelling them, and feeling very happy, until he came to the place where Eeyore was.

Date	Name	Address

Date	Name	Address

Date	Name	Address

Date	Name	Address

Owl took Christopher Robin's notice from Rabbit
and looked at it nervously. He could spell his own
name WOL, and he could spell Tuesday so that
you knew it wasn't Wednesday.

Date	Name	Address

"It's coming!" said Pooh.
"Are you *sure* it's mine?"
squeaked Piglet excitedly.
"Yes, because it's grey.
A big grey one. Here it
comes! A very – big –
grey — Oh, no, it isn't,
it's Eeyore."
And out floated Eeyore.

Date	Name	Address

Date	Name	Address

Date	Name	Address

"Oh, Eeyore, you *are* wet!" said Piglet, feeling him.
Eeyore shook himself, and asked somebody to explain
to Piglet what happened when you had been inside
a river for quite a long time.

Date	Name	Address

Date	Name	Address

"Well," said Pooh, "I've got to go home for something, and so has Piglet, because we haven't had it yet, and — "

"I'll come and watch you," said Christopher Robin.

So he went home with Pooh, and watched him for quite a long time . . .

Date	Name	Address

Tigger kept disappearing, and then when you thought
he wasn't there, there he was again, saying, "I say, come on,"
and before you could say anything, there he wasn't.

Date	Name	Address

Date	Name	Address

Pooh looked at his two paws. He knew that one of them was the right, and he knew that when you had decided which one of them was the right, then the other one was the left, but he never could remember how to begin.

Date	Name	Address

Date	Name	Address

There was a loud cracking noise.

"Look out!" cried Pooh. "Mind the clock! Out of the way, Piglet.
Piglet, I'm falling on you!"

"Help!" cried Piglet.

Pooh's side of the room was slowly tilting upwards and his chair began sliding down on
Piglet's. The clock slithered gently along the mantelpiece, collecting vases on the way,
until they all crashed together on to what had once been the floor, but was now trying to
see what it looked like as a wall.

Date	Name	Address

The wind was against them now, and Piglet's ears streamed behind him like banners as he fought his way along.

Date	Name	Address

Date	Name	Address

In a corner of the room, the table-cloth
began to wriggle. Then it wrapped itself
into a ball and rolled across the room.
Then it jumped up and down once or twice,
and put out two ears.

Date	Name	Address

Date	Name	Address

Pooh had wandered into the Hundred Acre Wood, and was standing in front of what had once been Owl's House. It didn't look at all like a house now; it looked like a tree which had been blown down; and as soon as a house looks like that, it is time you tried to find another one.

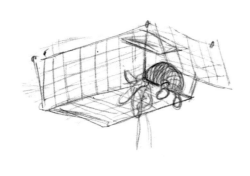
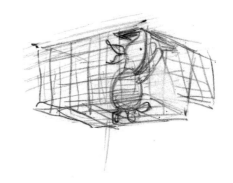

Date	Name	Address

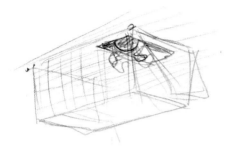
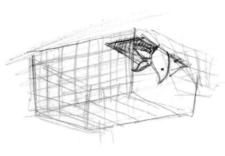
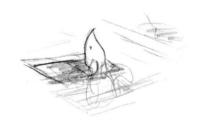

Date	Name	Address

"If you save us all, it will be a Very Grand Thing
to talk about afterwards, and perhaps I'll make up a Song,
and people will say 'It was so grand what Piglet did
that a Respectful Pooh Song was made about it!'"

Date	Name	Address

Kanga was down below tying the things on,
and calling out to Owl, "You won't want this
dirty old dish-cloth any more, will you,
and what about this carpet, it's all in holes,"
and Owl was calling back indignantly,
"Of course I do!"

Date	Name	Address

Date	Name	Address

"A Knight?"

"Oh, was that it?" said Pooh. "I thought it was a — Is it as Grand as a King and Factors and all the other things you said?"

"Well, it's not as grand as a King," said Christopher Robin, and then, as Pooh seemed disappointed, he added quickly, "but it's grander than Factors."

"Could a Bear be one?"

"Of course he could!" said Christopher Robin. "I'll make you one." And he took a stick and touched Pooh on the shoulder, and said, "Rise, Sir Pooh de Bear, most faithful of all my Knights."

He wondered if being a Faithful Knight
meant that you just went on being faithful
without being told things.

Date	Name	Address

Christopher Robin is going.
At least I think he is.
Where?
Nobody knows.
But he is going —
I mean he goes
(To rhyme with "knows")

Date	Name	Address

Do we care?
(To rhyme with "where")
We do
Very much.

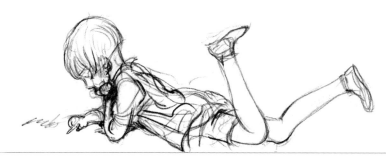

Date	Name	Address

Christopher Robin, goodbye,
I
(Good)
I
And all your friends
Sends —

Date	Name	Address

I mean all your friend
Send —
*(Very awkward this, it keeps
going wrong.)*
Well, anyhow, we send
Our love.

Date	Name	Address

US TWO
Wherever I am, there's always Pooh,
There's always Pooh and Me.
Whatever I do, he wants to do . . .

Date	Name	Address

"Where are you going today?" says Pooh:
"Well, that's very odd 'cos I was too."

Date	Name	Address

"Let's go together," says Pooh, says he.
"Let's go together," says Pooh.

Date	Name	Address

Date	Name	Address

Date	Name	Address

"What's twice eleven?" I said to Pooh,
("Twice what?" said Pooh to Me.)
"I *think* it ought to be twenty-two."

"Just what I think myself," said Pooh.
"It wasn't an easy sum to do,
But that's what it is," said Pooh, said he.
"That's what it is," said Pooh.

Date	Name	Address

Date	Name	Address

Date	Name	Address

Date	Name	Address

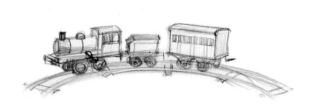

Date	Name	Address

E. H. Shepard

"Waiting at the window"
(Now we are Six)
1927

So wherever I am, there's always Pooh,
There's always Pooh and Me.
"What would I do?" I said to Pooh,
"If it wasn't for you,"

Date	Name	Address

Date	Name	Address

. . . and Pooh said: "True,
It isn't much fun for One, but Two
Can stick together," says Pooh, says he.
"That's how it is," says Pooh.

Date	Name	Address

Date	Name	Address

Date	Name	Address

First published in Great Britain in 1994 by
Methuen Children's Books
an imprint of Reed Children's Books
Michelin House, 81 Fulham Road, London SW3 6RB
and Auckland, Melbourne, Singapore and Toronto
Copyright © 1994 by Michael John Brown, Peter Janson-Smith,
Roger Hugh Vaughan Charles Morgan and Timothy Michael Robinson,
Trustees of the Pooh Properties.
Published under licence from The Walt Disney Company
Text by A. A. Milne and line drawings by E. H. Shepard
From *Winnie-the-Pooh*, first published 1926, *The House at Pooh Corner*,
first published 1928 and *Now We are Six*, first published 1927
copyright under the Berne Convention

ISBN 0 416 19005 7

Printed in Great Britain by BPC Paulton Books Ltd.